Pokemon!
The Best Websites
and Factoids

An Unofficial, Independent
Internet Guide

Lightning Rod Ltd.
Port Orchard 📖 Seattle

Pokemon! The Best Websites and Factoids:
An Unofficial, Independent Internet Guide
copyright 2001 and published by
Lightning Rod Limited

ISBN 1-59092-021-X
First Edition January 2002
9 8 7 6 5 4 3 2
Cover, interior and series design by
Buster Blue of BlueArtisans

Lightning Rod Limited is a division of Windstorm Creative, a six imprint, international organization involved in publishing books in all genres including electronic publications; producing games, toys, video and audio cassettes as well as producing theatre, film and visual arts events. The lightning bolt on the web logo is a trademark of Windstorm Creative.

Lightning Rod Limited
7419 Ebbert Drive Southeast
Port Orchard WA 98367
360-769-7174
pokemon@arabyfair.com
www.arabyfair.com

How Did these Websites Get in this Guide?

The Direct Hits! series editor, Talis Pelucir, and the Direct Hits! compilers view hundreds of websites on every topic we publish. From these they select the ones that offer exclusive, unique or rare information. These are what we call the best sites on the web.

Want Your Website Considered for this Guide?

To have your website considered for the next edition of this guide, just mail your URL to Lightning Rod with the name of the guide you want to be included in. Alternatively, you can email us at directhits@arabyfair. com.

Have a Cool Factoid for Us?

Send your factoid to us by mail or email and tell us where you heard or read it. We'll check it out and consider it for publication in the next edition of this guide.

Looking for Other *Direct Hits!* Guides?

Go to www.arabyfair.com and click on the Internet Guides link to purchase other guides.

Found a Dead Link?

Hey, the web is always changing so if you find a dead link in this guide tell us about it by mail or email so we can replace it. Suggest a replacement link — even your own site! Help us bring you the most up-to-date guides possible.

Editor's Series Dedication

To all those intrepid webmasters and mistresses who have dedicated so much time and love to creating websites for your favorite shows and stars, thanks for giving me countless pleasureable hours on the web. Additionally, I appreciate all those who have supported — and made possible — unofficial guides over the past years.

Editor's Biography

Talis Pelucir lives near Ullswater, England with his wife and children.

Other Great Unofficial, Independent Books by Lightning Rod

The *Babylon 5: Crusade* Episode Guide
The *Farscape* Episode Guide for Season One
The *Farscape* Episode Guide for Season Two
The *Farscape* Episode Guide for Season Three
The *Xena: Warrior Princess* Episode Guide
for Season One
The *Gene Roddenberry's Andromeda* Episode Guide
for Season One

In the *Direct Hits!* Series
Pop Culture Imprint

Gene Roddenberry's Andromeda
Babylon 5
Babylon 5: Crusade
Buffy The Vampire Slayer
Charmed
Dark Shadows
Doctor Who
Farscape
James Bond
Magic: The Gathering
MST3K
Pokemon
Red Dwarf
Sailor Moon
The Sopranos
Stargate SG-1
Star Trek: The Original Series
Star Trek: Voyager
Xena: Warrior Princess
The X-Files

Non-Fiction Imprint

Gillian Anderson
Sandra Bullock
Stephen King
Online Bookstores
Mars

Pokemon!
The Best Websites
and Factoids

Gengar's Tower
Download a free Pokémon simulator here, get your questions answered, check out the picture gallery and walkthrough.
http://maxpages.com/gengartower

Factoid: As of December 2001, there were more than three thousand Pokémon sites on the web.

Here There Be Pikachus!
Battle your Pokémon here, visit the Pokémon Center, post on message boards and more.
http://www.unca.edu/~jsallen/Pokémon. html

Factoid: As of November 2001, there were three Pokémon animated films.

Japanime.com

This toy store will rock your world. Here's 50-some incredible Pokémon items (toys, blankets, games, videos and much, much more) straight from Japan. All shipments are traceable, insured and arrive within 3 - 5 days.

http://www.japanime.com

Factoid: There were originally only 151 Pokémon "documented," now, more than 250 others have been added to the universal Pokedex.

Mew Catcher's Brand Spankin' New X-Files

Some news here about the administrator's travels to various conventions as well as message boards game codes and more. Be sure to check out *The X-Files* link which reveals everything you've suspected about Pokémon, but could never prove. And they say you can't uncover conspiracy! http://expage.com/page/mewsxfiles

Factoid: Though perhaps not the most favorite of all the Pokémon, Pikachu is easily the most recognizable to the general public. This is probably because Pikachu stars along with Ash in the television show, the comic book and in the Nintendo GameBoy game Pokémon: Yellow.

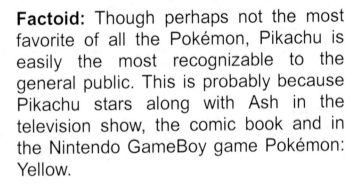

Pokéland: Unofficial American Pokémon Site

A wealth of information here. Current news on Nintendo games, including Snap and Pinball as well as the GameBoy games. You can also print out a handful of drawings to color. The fan art section includes an opportunity for fans to send in images of themselves as Pokémon trainers as well as a number of original images. There's a fan club, letters section and a download section (usually only available on Saturday and Sunday). Also includes quite a bit of pertinent information on collectable cards.

http://209.41.117.70/pokeland/home.htm

Factoid: Pokémon trading cards were offered from Burger King with a trading card game offered from Wizards of the Coast.

Pokémon

Pokémon adoption center for the original 150 Pokémon.
http://tinpan.fortunecity.com/kowalski/828/adoptaPokémon.htm

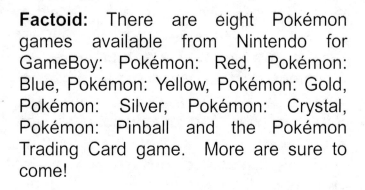

Factoid: There are eight Pokémon games available from Nintendo for GameBoy: Pokémon: Red, Pokémon: Blue, Pokémon: Yellow, Pokémon: Gold, Pokémon: Silver, Pokémon: Crystal, Pokémon: Pinball and the Pokémon Trading Card game. More are sure to come!

Pokémon Adoption Agency

Site offers all 150 original Pokémon for adoption. You can also adopt a "Mystery Egg" Pikachu that will hatch -- interesting.
http://www.geocities.com/Tokyo/Gulf/1915/index.html

Factoid: There are five Pokémon games for Nintendo's 64 system: Pokémon Stadium, Pokémon Snap!, Hey You! Pikachu!, Pokémon Stadium2 and Pokémon Puzzle League.

Pokémon Fan Club

Message boards and chat rooms. Membership is free. To preview the site without becoming a member, sign in as a guest. Vast array of subjects, lots of comments and ideas about Pokémon. http://www.delphi.com/Pokémonclub/

Factoid: For their October 30 – November 11, 1999 issue *TV Guide* released four collectable Pokémon covers featuring Meowth with Togapi, Geodude with Psyduck, Exaggcute with Pikachu and Voltorb with Charmander.

Pokémon Illustration Marathon

Downloadable illustrations of many of the 150 Pokémon with new ones added regularly. The site owner (and illustrator) is a twenty-five- year-old Tokyo resident, Daisuke Matsumura, working with Adobe Illustrator and Microsoft's Photoshop among others.
http://www.fsinet.or.jp/~pokesen/ illusthome.html

Factoid: Viz Comics is the publisher of the Pokémon comic books. Their website is www.viz.com. Did you know that mini versions of the comics were tucked inside some of the early Pokémon videos?

Pokémon League

A very comprehensive page. Great logo at the top of this page. In the site owner's own words: "On this site you will find information on: The Game, The Cartoon, Toys, Previews, FAQs, Links to other Pokémon sites, and Downloads." You can also adopt Pokémon here, read fan fiction, look up Pokémon TV listings, link to an episode guide, read about current and forthcoming games for GameBoy, Nin64 and more.

http://surf.to/PokeLeague

Factoid: There are two virtual Pikachu pet toys. Pokémon Pikachu has black 'n' white graphics and Pokémon Pikachu 2 has color graphics and the ability to send "watts" to Pokémon: Gold and Pokémon: Silver to earn special items.

Pokémon Sounds Page

Lots of great sounds here both from the show and the game.
http://members.tripod.com/~jules44/Poke/poke.html

Factoid: The Pokémon comics were first released by Shogakukan Inc. in Japan. The story and art for both the Japanese and the English version were created by Toshihiro Ono.

Pokémon TC for Half-Life

"The Pokémon TC for Half-Life is a modification of the Half-Life engine that will recreate an authentic Pokémon theme in full 3D. You can battle with Pokémon and other trainers in a fully interactive environment." They are looking for modelers and programmers. http://www.converted2.com/Pokémon/

Factoid: Pokémon was created in Japan and first appeared in 1995 as a GameBoy game.

Pokémon Virtual Postcard

Send and pick up your virtual mail here. Offers sixteen free postcards for sending to your Pokémon pals. Part of Chari's Pokémon Potpourri.
http://www.geocities.com/Tokyo/ Gulf/2433/pokecard.html

Factoid: In Japan, Pokémon is called Pocket Monsters.

Pokémon Unofficial HQ
Lots of information here. Plot descriptions for the latest Pokémon movies, gaming help, 3D pictures, screen shots, world map, battle chart, bios for the TV characters and more.
http://unofficialpoke.cjb.net/

Factoid: When playing Pokémon: Red or Pokémon: Blue for the first time, it makes things easier if you have two great books to help with hints, tips, maps and more. They are the *Pokémon Player's Guide* from Nintendo and *Pokémon Trainer's Survival Guide* from Sandwich Island Publications.

Pokémon World

Official Nintendo site. Find what TV stations broadcast the show and read a description of the videos. In-depth online strategy guide for GameBoy game including hints, best bets, FAQ and battle chart. Site also includes detailed encyclopedia pages on most Pokémon, an online Pokédex, links to buy the comics, videos, GameBoy games and the CCG, info about the humans of the Pokémon universe as well as downloadable trainer badges and five different wallpaper images.
http://www.Pokémon.com/

Factoid: Did you know there's a Pokémon cereal? Well, there is! It even has Pokémon-shaped marshmallows.

Ultimate Pokémon Page, The

Information on the TV show as well as on the GameBoy Game. The TV show section features an episode list and character profiles. The red and blue game information is quite extensive, but the green, yellow and gold/silver versions as well as pinball only have screen captures. Fan fiction, downloads, fan art round out this extensive site.

http://Pokémon.therpgn.com

Factoid: Pokémon is pronounced Poh-kay-mahn.

With Love Pikachu

This site features fan fiction, a list of the TV episodes, the Pika Pika Picasso Art Gallery (fan art), a translation of the theme song into English (unfortunately the cute background makes the words very hard to read) and more. The Pikachu in Iowa sequence is quite funny: it features a small Pikachu at various sites in an unnamed Iowa town. The Pokémon in American Names section is confusing for the English-only speaker. Site also shows photos of Pokémon merchandise, but it's not for sale here.
http://www.na.rim.or.jp/~shou/Pokémon.html

Factoid: In America, the first two GameBoy games were Red and Blue. In Japan, the first two were called Red and Green, but they were actually the same game as the American versions.

Wizards of the Coast
A site dedicated to the Pokémon trading card game produced by Wizards of the Coast, the site includes strategy tips, a game arena, current news about this game as well as their other products.
http://www.wizards.com/Pokémon/

Factoid: The *Pokémon Player's Guide* comes with 150 small Pokémon stickers to help players keep track of the Pokémon they've caught in the Red, Blue or Yellow versions.

Free Pokémon Card Club
With more than 350 members, this club has lots of information on purchasing, trading and collecting cards.
http://clubs.yahoo.com/clubs/freePokémoncardclub

Factoid: At the height of the Pokémon craze, the Saturday morning television show ranked number one for two-to-eleven-year-olds.

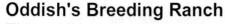

Oddish's Breeding Ranch

This club is quite active. Post photos, chat and exchange information with other trainers here.

http://clubs.yahoo.com/clubs/ oddishsbreedingranch

Factoid: Ash Ketchum is twelve-years-old at the beginning of the Pokémon saga.

Pallet Town Pokémon Gym

A club where members catch and raise Pokémon, members can also participate in quests and tournaments. Has over 180 members.

http://clubs.yahoo.com/clubs/ pallettownPokémongym

Factoid: Sales of Pokémon products in Japan total more than 4.5 billion dollars.

Pikachu's Pokémon Battle Stadium

A medium sized club of about forty members, you can battle your Pokémon online here, participate in chats and post on the message boards.

http://clubs.yahoo.com/clubs/ pikachusPokémonbattlestadium

Factoid: Pokémon was created by Satoshi Tajiri of Game Freak Inc. in 1995. He was inspired by insects he used to catch as a boy and by monsters on Japanese television shows.

Pokémon Breeders Club

An active online community of other Pokémon trainers, this club is features online chats and discussion boards. The focus is on tactics and evolving your Pokémon to their best advantage. Administered by Gengar.

http://clubs.yahoo.com/clubs/ Pokémonbreedersclub

Factoid: Pokémon has become the most popular series of games for GameBoy in the entire history of Nintendo games.

Pokémon Card Trading Center
Looking for that hard-to-find card? Have some cards to sell? Buyers and sellers exchange information here. Remember, this is not an auction site and therefore is not regulated.
http://clubs.yahoo.com/clubs/
Pokémoncardtradingzone

Factoid: In 1999, the sales of Pokémon toys out-sold *Star Wars* toys five-to-one at the famous toy story, F.A.O. Schwartz

Pokémon Card Trades and Sells

A club for buyers, sellers and traders of both the Japanese and American cards. With more than 180 members, this club also has a weekly chat on Thursdays and contests.

http://clubs.yahoo.com/clubs/ Pokémoncardtradesandsells

Factoid: In 1999, a group of parents filed a class action lawsuit against Nintendo and Wizards of the Coast because they felt that buying randomly packed booster packs in the hopes of getting a rare card was gambling.

Pokémon Center's Club, The

With over 600 members, this is the largest Yahoo club. A clearinghouse for all kinds of information on Pokémon with active message boards and chats.
http://clubs.yahoo.com/clubs/thePokémoncentersclub

Factoid: The National Parenting Center awarded the Pokémon Trading Card Game its official Seal of Approval in 1999.

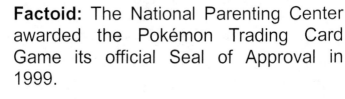

Porygon

Come here to meet Porygon, a Pokémon who exists entirely of programming code and is able to move freely through cyberspace. This club has over 60 members and offers regular Saturday battles and daily chats.
http://clubs.yahoo.com/clubs/porygon

Factoid: One of the most valuable Pokémon trading cards was released by Wizards of the Coast in their Base Set. The first editing of "Charizard" is now worth more than $240.00.

Rocket Battle Arena
A site dedicated primarily to "wiping out anti-Pokémon clubs," you can also receive a newsletter, cheat codes and more.
http://clubs.yahoo.com/clubs/therocketbattlearena

Factoid: Looking for a good book to figure out the value of your Pokémon trading cards? Try this one: Collector's Value Guide: Pokémon published by Checker Bee Publishing.